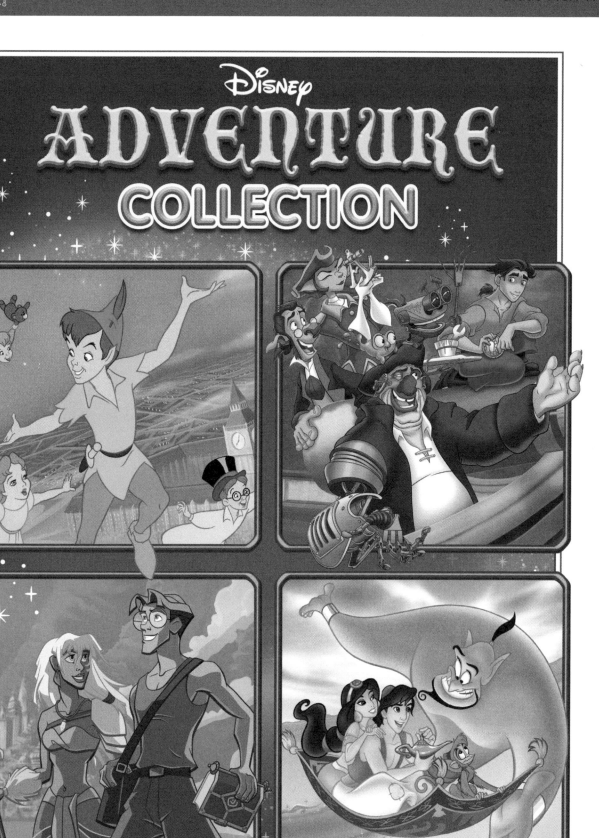

Disney
ADVENTURE
COLLECTION

Bendon Publishing, International
Ashland, Ohio

D1319481

Disney
ADVENTURE
COLLECTION

Table of Contents

FLASH CARD INSTRUCTIONS

The flash cards at the end of each story will help your child learn to recognize and practice frequently used words. First, carefully cut out the flash cards. Then, choose three to five cards at a time. Say the word on each card. Then, ask your child to repeat each word. Once your child masters these words, move through the pile in the same manner, continuing to review the words learned earlier.

There are a few other ways for you and your child to use these flash cards for extra practice. Here are a few suggestions:

- Pick the Word—Lay out 5-10 flash cards on a table. Then, say one of the words on the cards. Ask your child to point to the word you've said.
- Make a Sentence—Invite your child to make a sentence from the sight word cards. Have your child look at the illustrations in the story for ideas. Then, have your child choose another card and substitute it for one of the cards in the sentence. Ask your child how the new word changes the meaning of the sentence.
- My Own Sight Words—Have your child make his or her own sight word cards using the writing lines on the back of the cards. Help your child write words that he or she might use regularly, such as family names, your street, your town, or your state. Once your child is able to identify and recognize these words, add them to the "Make a Sentence" game above.

The flash cards in this collection can also be a useful tool as your child completes the activities at the end of each story. If a particular activity seems difficult for your child, use the flash cards to practice the activity first before your child writes.

Walt Disney's
Peter Pan

Adapted by Linda Armstrong

Table of Contents

"Take that, you dirty rotten old pirate," cried John Darling. He waved an old wooden sword at his brother Michael.

"You be the pirate. It is my turn to be Peter Pan," protested Michael.

Just **then**, their sister Wendy **came** in. "That is enough of that," she said. "If you get right into bed, I will tell you a new story."

John and Michael dived under the covers. They loved to hear Wendy's stories about Peter Pan.

Later, after they were all asleep, a figure dressed all in green zoomed **down** over the city. It was the real Peter Pan! **He** was searching for the Darling's house. When he spotted the **right** roof, he circled around.

Then he came right down.

"Come with me to Never Land," Peter Pan said. The sleepy children yawned and rubbed their eyes.

"How do we get there?" asked Michael.

"We fly, of course," Peter said, zipping around the room.

"Then we cannot go," said Wendy sadly. "We do not know how to fly."

"Flying is easy," Peter Pan said. "Just think happy thoughts."

Wendy, John, and Michael thought very happy thoughts. Peter Pan zipped and zoomed **over** their heads. Tinker Bell sprinkled **them** with pixie dust. **It fell down all** over the room.

It fell down all over them.

Soon, Wendy, John, and Michael were zipping and zooming around. They could fly just like Peter Pan.

"See, **I** told **you** it was easy," Peter **said**. "Now, off to Never Land. I **will** show you the way."

Peter Pan zoomed right out the window. He zipped past the second star on the right, then straight on until morning. Before they knew it, they were right above Never Land.

Captain Hook was out on the deck of his pirate ship. **He** was working on a plan to **get** rid of Peter Pan for good.

"I will get you, Peter Pan," he said.

The children zoomed down to the island. All of Peter's friends were there to meet them.

"Come on," said the Lost Boys. "We **will** explore the island." John and Michael marched off into the woods with them.

"Come on, Wendy," said Peter. "**I** have so much to show you." Peter and Wendy headed for the mermaid pool.

Meanwhile, Captain Hook started to carry out his evil plan. It depended on Princess **Tiger Lily**. She was Peter Pan's friend, and everybody knew it. Hook and his first mate grabbed Tiger Lily. They tied her up, stashed her in a rowboat, and rowed away from the shore. The ropes hurt her hands. They did **not** care.

"Tell us where Pan's hideout is," Hook **said**.

"I will not," Tiger Lily said.

Peter Pan and Wendy spotted **Tiger Lily** in the rowboat.

"What is going on?" Wendy asked.

"Maybe we should find out," Peter said.

They followed the rowboat to Skull Rock.

Peter saw the pirates take Tiger Lily ashore. **He** zoomed after them. "Let her go," he said.

Captain Hook laughed an evil laugh. "Says who?" he said.

"Says Peter Pan," Peter said. He raised his sword.

The pirate captain grinned an evil grin. "I **saved** this one for you," he said. He swung his sword at Peter.

Splash! Captain Hook fell off a cliff into the ocean. Peter swooped down.

He saved Tiger Lily.

Captain Hook was furious.

"I will **get** even with Peter Pan if it is the last thing I do," he said. He sent for his first mate.

"Get Tinker Bell, and bring her here," he ordered.

When his first mate brought Tinker Bell, Hook tricked her. She told Hook where Peter's secret hideout was. She **could not** stop herself. Then she escaped.

The pirates raced straight for the hideout. **They** snatched Wendy and her brothers. The pirates grabbed the Lost Boys, too. They hauled them **away** to the ship. Then they tied them to the mast.

They could not get away.

The pirates left a gift for Peter Pan. It had a note from Wendy.

Peter showed the gift to Tinker Bell. "Look what Wendy left me," he said. He started to open it.

Tinker Bell stopped him. The gift box had a bomb inside. Peter and Tinker Bell **got** out **of** there just in time.

Boom! The bomb exploded.

Peter and Tinker Bell zoomed **out** to rescue their friends. Peter cut the ropes and set the children free. While the children fought the pirate crew, **Peter Pan** chased Captain Hook **way** up in **the** sails.

"Now I have you!" said Captain Hook when Peter lost his sword.

"Do not be so sure," said Peter Pan.

The captain swung his big, sharp sword as hard as he could.

Peter Pan got out of the way.

Peter Pan leaped up **behind** Hook and got the pirate flag. He wrapped Captain Hook up in it. Then he took the captain's sword away.

"Please, give me one more chance," Captain Hook begged.

Peter let **him** go.

Then Hook attacked him, but the evil captain lost his balance and fell.

The crocodile was waiting **right** below in the water. Hook barely escaped the crocodile's snapping jaws. Hook raced across the waves so fast he was almost running.

The crocodile was right behind him.

"We will not see those pirates for a while," said Peter.

"No," said Wendy. "We really showed them."

Then she said, "I'm sorry, Peter. I wish we could stay, but **it** is time to go home."

"I know," he said. Then Tinker Bell sprinkled pixie dust over the ship. It rose up and sailed across the sky.

Later, Wendy's mother and father came in to check on the children.

"We went to Never Land tonight," Wendy said. "We fought pirates and saved a princess."

Wendy could tell they did not believe her.

Then she **saw** something outside the window. She shouted and pointed. **They all** ran to look. A pirate ship sailed across the moon.

They all saw it.

Read the words in the box. Then read the sentences. Find the word in the box that correctly completes each sentence. Write the word on the line.

_____

He _____ right over.

He was _____.

He fell _____.

_____ he came down.

right
came
Then
down

Say the word at the top of each box. Then fill in the missing letters.

fell

fe___ ___ ___

___ ___ ll

all

___ ___ ll

a ___ ___ ___

over

___ ___ v ___ r

o ___ e ___

them

___ ___ ___ ___

___ ___ ___ em

th ___ ___ ___

27

Trace the name with your pencil. Then write the name on your own.

Say the word at the top of each box. Then fill in the missing letters.

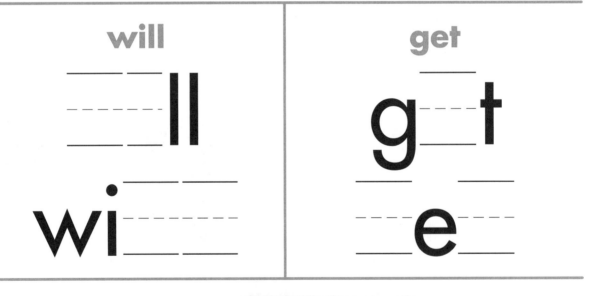

will	get
__ __ ll	g __ t
wi __ __	__ e __

28

Trace the name with your pencil. Then write the name on your own.

Tiger Lily

Read the words in the box. Then read the sentences. Find the word in the box that correctly completes each sentence. Write the word on the line.

He _____ I could get it.

_____ came right over.

I will _____ get it.

He _____ get them.

| **not** |
| **said** |
| **will** |
| **I** |

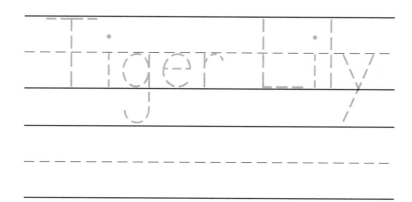

Say the word at the top of each box. Then fill in the missing letters.

he	saved
h___ ___	___ ___ ___ **ved**
___ **e**	___ **v** ___

Read the words in the box. Then read the sentences. Find the word in the box that correctly completes each sentence. Write the word on the line.

_____ saved them.

He _____ Tiger Lily.

saved
He

Say the word at the top of each box. Then fill in the missing letters.

they

th___
___ey

could

c___ld
cou___

not

n___t
___o

away

a___ay
aw___

Say the word at the top of each box. Then fill in the missing letters.

got

g__t

__o__

out

___t

ou__

Read the words in the box. Then read the sentences. Find the word in the box that correctly completes each sentence. Write the word on the line.

_____

Peter Pan _____ them out.

He came right _____.

It was the right _____.

He saw _____ way out.

the

got

way

out

Trace the word with your pencil. Then write the word on your own.

crocodile

Read the words in the box. Then read the sentences. Find the word in the box that correctly completes each sentence. Write the word on the line.

Peter Pan was _____ him.

He was _____ behind Peter Pan.

It _____ not right.

They saved _____.

| behind |
| was |
| him |
| right |

Say the word at the top of each box. Then fill in the missing letters.

saw	**it**
sa__	__t
__aw	i__

Read the words in the box. Then read the sentences. Find the word in the box that correctly completes each sentence. Write the word on the line.

He _____ all of them.

_____ saw it.

_____ was not Tiger Lily.

They _____ got out.

all
They
It
saw

all

away

behind

came

could

crocodile

down

fell

get

got

he

him

I

it

not

of

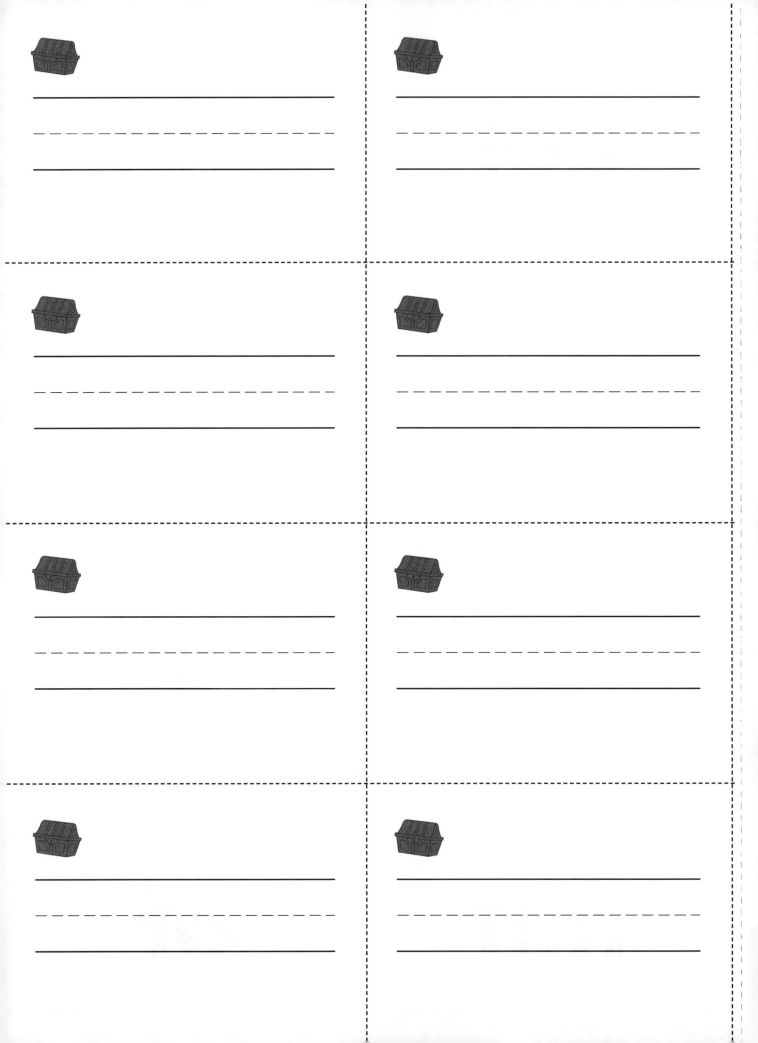

out

over

Peter Pan

right

said

saved

saw

the

them

then

they

Tiger Lily

was

way

will

you

DISNEY'S
RETURN TO
NEVER LAND

Adapted by Linda Armstrong

DISNEY's
RETURN TO
NEVER LAND

Table of Contents

It had been many years since her trip to Never Land, but Wendy never forgot it. When she grew up, she had children of her own. She loved to tell Danny and Jane stories about Peter Pan and Never Land. She always ended the stories the same way.

"**I will** always believe in you, Peter Pan," she **said**.

Jane loved her mother's stories, until her father went off to fight in the war.

"Your mother and little brother need you, Jane," her father told her. "I want you to take good care of them while I am gone."

"I will," Jane said.

After that, Jane thought she was too grown up for **Never Land**. She had no time for fun. She **took** everything very seriously. **Then** one night she found out that she and **her** brother had to go **away to** the country. Because of the war, the city was too dangerous for children.

"No, I am not going," she said.

"Danny will need someone to tell him stories about Peter Pan," Wendy said. "We will be back together soon. You just need a little faith."

"I know, faith, trust, and pixie dust," Jane said. "Those are just words. Stories will not stop the war or bring Daddy home. Peter Pan is not even real."

But after Jane fell asleep, Captain Hook came in through the window. **He** thought Jane was Wendy. He put her in a big bag.

Then he took her away to Never Land.

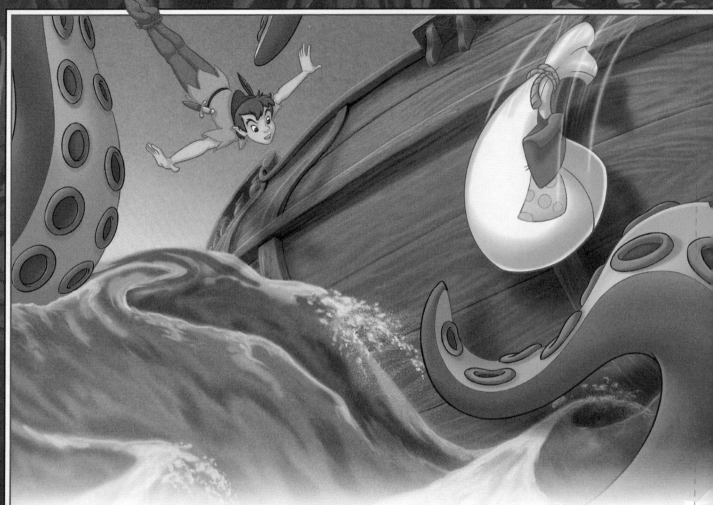

Captain Hook laughed an evil laugh. Then he said, "**I believe** this is the best plan yet. Peter Pan will try to save Wendy. He **cannot** escape from the octopus. I will be rid of him for good."

Hook's first mate dumped some fish into the water. A huge octopus came up to eat the fish. Then Hook picked up the sack with Jane inside. He dropped **it** right on top of the octopus.

Peter Pan zoomed down out of the sky and went after the sack. Hook was overjoyed. He thought the octopus had eaten both of them, but he was wrong. Peter Pan came flying out of the water carrying the sack. When Peter opened the sack, he was surprised.

"You are not Wendy," he said.

"Wendy is my mother," Jane **said**.

"I cannot believe it," Peter Pan said.

Peter Pan dropped **Jane** down the chute to his hideout. The Lost Boys were waiting for Peter to come back. They stared at Jane.

"This is Jane," Peter explained. "She is going to tell us stories."

"**I** am not good at telling stories," Jane protested.

"We do not mind, **because** we are not good at listening to them," the Lost Boys said.

"I cannot stay here. I have to go home," Wendy said. She went down to the beach. She built a raft out of wood and put a sail on it.

"You **cannot** get home that way," Peter Pan **said**.

When Jane's boat sank, Peter Pan helped her get back to shore. "The only way you can get home is to **fly**," he said.

"Then I will be here forever," Jane said miserably.

"Why?" Peter asked.

"Because I cannot fly," Jane said.

Peter tried to teach Jane to fly, **but** she did not trust **him**. Even when Tinker Bell showered her with Pixie Dust, Jane did not have any faith in her ability, so it **did** not work.

"I do not **like** it here. I do **not** believe in pixie dust or fairies. I do not believe in any of you," Jane said.

She ran away into the forest. Captain Hook found her there.

"I will help you, if you help me," he said. "Peter Pan **took** my treasure. I cannot leave this island without **it**. Just blow on this whistle when you find the treasure, and I will take you home."

Captain Hook handed the whistle to Jane.

She did not like him, but she took it.

When Jane found Peter and the boys, they were glad to see her. As Jane explored Never Land with them, she started to have fun.

They sat down to rest. "What would you like to do now?" Peter Pan asked.

Jane remembered Captain Hook. "How about a treasure hunt?" she asked.

"That is a great idea," Peter Pan said.

They all went in different directions, looking for the treasure. Jane found the treasure in Dead Man's Cave. **Then** Peter and the Lost Boys **came**.

"You found it!" Peter Pan said. "We are going to make you the first Lost Girl." All of the Lost Boys cheered.

Jane did not want to call **Captain Hook** after all. She threw the whistle away, but one of the Lost Boys found it and blew on it.

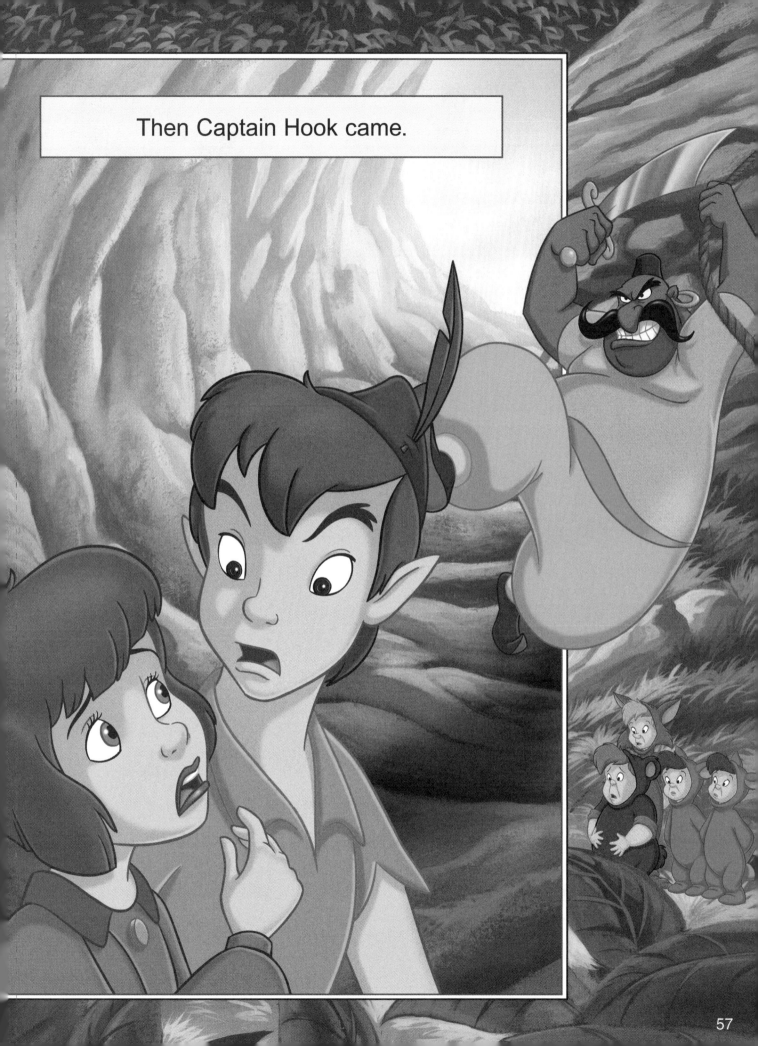

Then Captain Hook came.

Hook and his men captured Peter and the Lost Boys.
"Thank you, Jane," Captain Hook said.

"Did you help him **set** this trap, Jane?" Peter asked.

"Hook tricked me," Jane said, but Peter did not believe her.

Captain Hook took Peter and the Lost Boys to his ship.
They needed help to **free** themselves.

Jane knew that she could save **them** if only she could
fly. **She** had faith and trust. She just needed some pixie
dust. Jane raced back to the hideout. Tinker Bell sprinkled
pixie dust all over her.

Jane floated up into the air. She zoomed out to the pirate
ship. She found Peter and the Lost Boys.

She set them free.

The Lost Boys found Hook's treasure. They used slingshots to shoot jewels overboard. The pirates plunged into the water after the jewels. While fighting with Peter Pan, Hook lost his balance. He tumbled into the water **with** the rest of his crew.

It did not take long for the hungry octopus to find them.

Hook and his men swam **away** so fast they almost **flew**.

"**Jane**, I knew you could do it," **Peter Pan** said when they were safe on shore. "All you needed was faith, trust, and a little pixie dust."

"You were right all the time. I will always believe in you, Peter Pan," Jane said.

"Thank you," Peter said. "I'll take you home now."

The Lost Boys waved goodbye.

Jane flew away with Peter Pan.

Jane told Wendy all about her trip to **Never Land**. Then Jane went **to** her room, and Wendy went to the window to look at Peter's special star. Peter and Tinker Bell came to see her.

"You have changed," Peter said.

"Not really," Wendy said.

Just then, a car pulled up in front of the house. Jane saw the car first. She knew who it was. She dashed down the stairs and **flew** into her father's arms.

"Daddy, you are home!" she cried. Wendy and Danny **both** hurried to join her.

Peter Pan and Tinker Bell watched the happy family. Then **they** headed for the second star to the right, and went straight on until morning.

They both flew to Never Land.

63

Trace the name with your pencil. Then write the name on your own.

Say the word at the top of each box. Then fill in the missing letters.

her	away
___	___
___er	___way
h___	a___ay

Read the words in the box. Then read the sentences. Find the word in the box that correctly completes each sentence. Write the word on the line.

He _____ it.

She took it _____.

_____ flew away.

He took _____ away.

> **He**
> **away**
> **took**
> **her**

Trace the name with your pencil. Then write the name on your own.

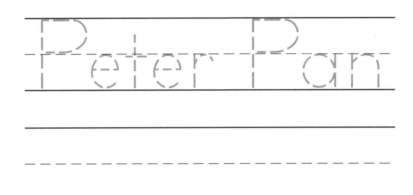

Read the words in the box. Then read the sentences. Find the word in the box that correctly completes each sentence. Write the word on the line.

| cannot |
| believe |
| it |
| said |

I did not _____ it.

Jane _____ believe it.

Jane _____ she did not believe it.

I said I did not like _____.

Say the word at the top of each box. Then fill in the missing letters.

because

___ ___ ___
___ ___ ___ cause

bec ___ ___ ___ se

cannot

___ ___ ___ ___

can ___ ___ ___

___ ___ ___ ___

___ ___ ___ not

fly

___ ___ ___
___ ___ y

fl ___

said

___ ___
sa ___ ___

___ ___ id

Read the words in the box. Then read the sentences. Find the word in the box that correctly completes each sentence. Write the word on the line.

_____

Jane _____ not like Peter Pan.

_____

_____ cannot fly.

It will _____ fly away.

She did not _____ him.

like

not

She

did

Trace the name with your pencil. Then write the name on your own.

Say the word at the top of each box. Then fill in the missing letters.

then	came
___ ___ en	___ a ___ e
th ___ ___ ___	c ___ m ___

69

Read the words in the box. Then read the sentences. Find the word in the box that correctly completes each sentence. Write the word on the line.

_____

Jane _____ them free.

_____

She cannot set it _____.

_____

She took _____.

_____

Then _____ set it free.

free
them
she
set

Say the word at the top of each box. Then fill in the missing letters.

with	flew
wi _ _ _	fl _ _ _
w _ th	_ _ _ ew

Read the words in the box. Then read the sentences. Find the word in the box that correctly completes each sentence. Write the word on the line.

_____

He _____ away.

| away |
| flew |
| with |

_____

Peter Pan flew _____.

_____

Jane took it _____ her.

Read the words in the box. Then read the sentences. Find the word in the box that correctly completes each sentence. Write the word on the line.

_____

They _____ flew away.

_____ like to fly.

He _____ away.

She did not like _____ fly.

both
flew
They
to

away

because

believe

both

but

came

cannot

Captain Hook

did

flew

fly

free

he

her

him

I

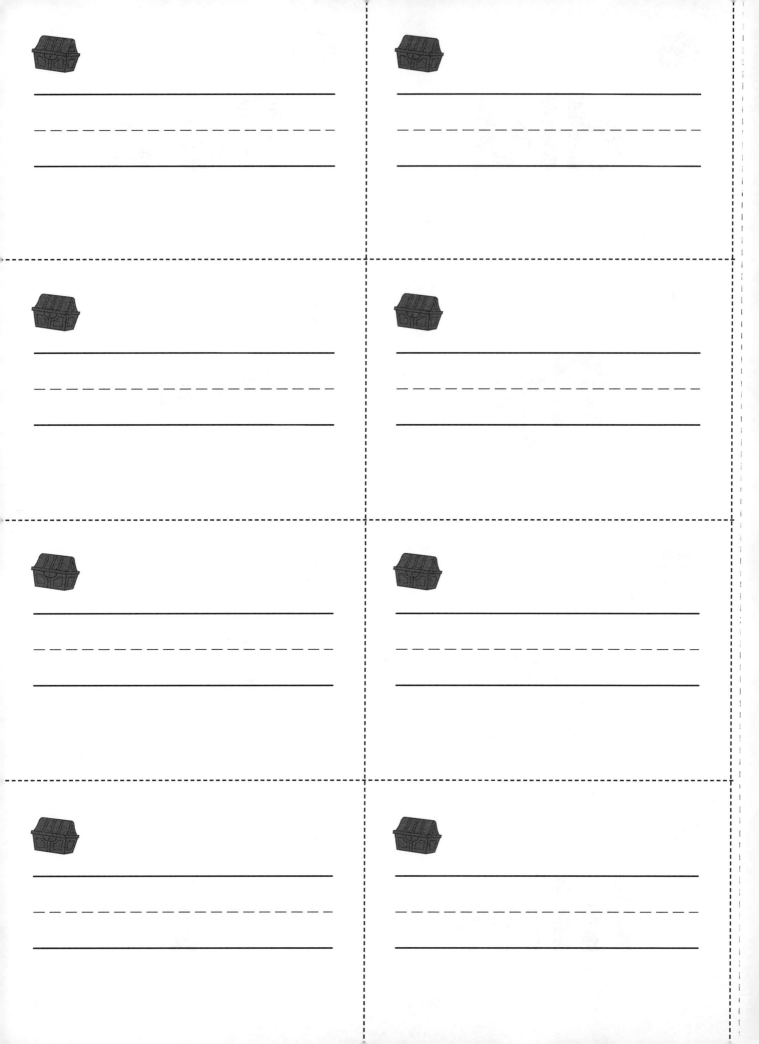

it	Jane
© Disney	© Disney

like	Never Land
© Disney	© Disney

not	Peter Pan
© Disney	© Disney

said	set
© Disney	© Disney

she

them

then

they

to

took

will

with

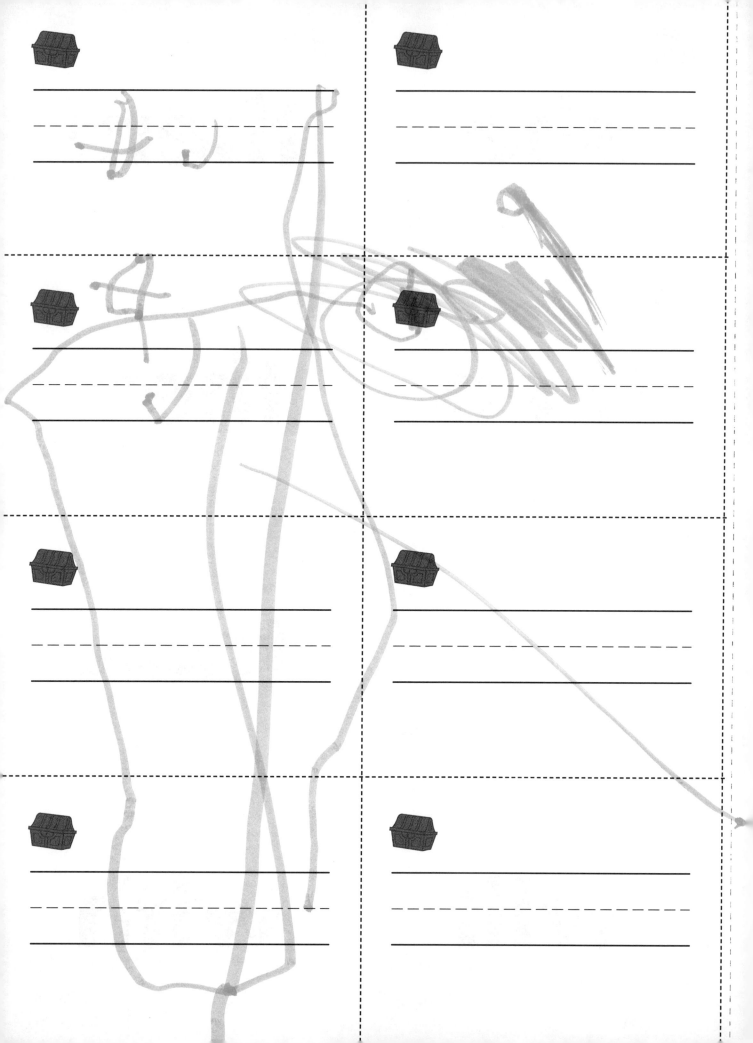

DISNEY'S
TREASURE PLANET

Adapted by Linda Armstrong

DISNEY's

TREASURE PLANET

Table of Contents

When an alien ship crashed on the planet Montressor, Jim Hawkins raced to help. Jim dragged the dying pilot into his mother's inn. The pilot handed Jim a strange sphere. "Beware the cyborg," **he said**. "Do not let him **find** this."

"What cyborg?" Jim asked, but the pilot had died.

Then Jim looked out the window. A band of pirates was heading for the inn. "**We** have to go," he yelled. "Run as fast as you **can**!"

Jim, his mother, and her friend Dr. Doppler escaped from the inn just before the pirates burned **it** to the ground. Safe in Dr. Doppler's observatory, Jim played around with the sphere the pilot had given him. Suddenly, it opened up and projected a huge map all around them. The map showed the way to Treasure Planet where the infamous Captain Flint had stored "the loot of a thousand worlds."

Dr. Doppler had been waiting his whole life for a chance like this. He promised to find a ship and hire a crew. He convinced Jim's mother that the trip would be good for the boy. Treasure Planet was waiting for them.

"We can find it," he said.

Dr. Doppler took **Jim** to the spaceport, and they boarded their ship, the *Legacy*. Captain Amelia and her first mate Mr. Arrow were waiting for them.

Dr. Doppler was very excited. He started to tell the captain about the map to Treasure Planet. Captain Amelia **did** not let him finish. She took Jim and Dr. Doppler into **her** cabin.

"I do **not like** this crew you hired," Captain Amelia said softly. "Do not let them know about this map." She took the map away from Jim and locked it up.

Jim did not like her.

"Mr. Arrow," Captain Amelia ordered, "take Jim down to the galley to meet John Silver, the ship's cook. Jim is going to be our new cabin boy."

"Cabin boy?" Jim muttered. **He** had not come on this trip to scrub floors and wash dirty pots.

"Glad to meet you, Jimbo," said John Silver, putting out his hand. Jim shuddered when he saw that Silver's arm was **gone**. A mechanical arm had replaced it. Silver had an artificial eye and a mechanical leg, too. He **was** a cyborg. Jim remembered the pilot's warning and decided to be careful.

Silver and his pet, Morph, kept Jim busy. As Jim worked, he learned about the ship. He was proud when he learned to tie knots better than John Silver.

Then, one day, the ship ran into a cosmic storm. Jim tied the lifelines that held the shipmates to the ship. When everything was calm again, Captain Amelia called out, "All hands accounted for, Mr. Arrow?" The first mate, Mr. Arrow, did not answer. His lifeline had come loose.

He was gone.

Jim said he had checked the lifelines, but nobody believed him. Silver told Jim that he **did** a good job and that Mr. Arrow's death was not his fault. Jim hugged Silver.

One morning, Morph snatched Jim's boot. Jim chased him into a fruit barrel in the galley. While Jim was in the barrel, he overheard a secret meeting between Silver and the crew.

Scroop, a spider-like alien, bragged about cutting Mr. Arrow's lifeline. Then he said, "Why **not** kill the rest of them?"

"Wait until we **have** the gold," Silver insisted.

Just then there was a shout on deck, "Planet ho!"

The pirates rushed up to see Treasure Planet. As soon as they were gone, Jim climbed out of the barrel and raced to warn the captain. Realizing that Jim had overheard the plan, Silver tried to grab him. When **he** could not stop Jim, Silver called to his friends, "We move now, lads!" The pirates raised their flag.

When Jim finally reached her office, Captain Amelia handed him **the map**. Just then, Morph snatched the map away, wanting to play. Jim caught Morph and got the map back. Then, Captain Amelia, Dr. Doppler, and Jim zoomed away to Treasure Planet in a longboat. The pirates fired a laser cannon at them, hitting the boat's sail. Although injured, Captain Amelia managed to land the boat safely. When she asked Jim for the map, he reached into his pocket.

He did not have the map.

Morph was in his pocket instead. Morph had changed himself to look and feel like the map. "Oh, no," Jim groaned. "That means the real map is still on the ship."

"That does not matter now," **said** Dr. Doppler. "Captain Amelia is hurt, and the pirates are coming. We need a place to hide."

As Jim looked for a hiding place, something jumped out of the bushes and hugged him. It was Captain Flint's old robot B.E.N.

"Do you know where the treasure is?" Jim asked, when he found out that the robot had worked for Flint.

"Treasure? **I** think I used to know, but my memory chip is missing," the robot said. **He** pointed to the back of his head.

Jim heard the pirates coming through the bushes. "**Do** you **have a place** to hide?" Jim asked.

B.E.N. nodded.

"I do have a place," he said.

Jim and his friends hid **in** B.E.N.'s home, an ancient tower on a hill. They were safe for a while, but Silver found them. Even though Silver had plotted against them, he did not wish them harm, but he did want the map to the treasure.

"I will be back for the map in the morning," the old pirate said.

After Silver left, Jim, Morph, and B.E.N. found the **place** where the pirates **put** their longboats. They took one and sailed back to the *Legacy*. Jim sneaked past Scroop and found the map. Just then, Scroop found him and grabbed him. At that moment, B.E.N. accidentally turned off the gravity field. Both Jim and Scroop drifted up into the sails. Jim grabbed a mast, but Scroop drifted away.

When Jim got back to Treasure Planet, he found Doppler and Amelia in the hands of the pirates. Silver and the pirates were waiting for him. Silver snatched the map from Jim, but **he** did not know how to make it work.

"Jimbo, if you care about your friends here, you will take us to the treasure," Silver said.

Silver and his pirates along with Jim and his friends took off in the longboat. Everyone except Amelia and Doppler followed Jim. Using the map, Jim led them to the edge of a cliff where a pattern was carved in the rock that matched the pattern on the map. Jim held **the map** above the pattern.

He put the map in place.

A huge triangular portal and a round controller appeared. The triangle was a door in space. Jim suddenly realized that Flint used **this** portal to travel to other planets and steal all of his treasure. But **he** still did not know where Flint had hidden the gold.

Jim and B.E.N. used what little they knew to figure out that the whole planet was a machine, and the treasure was inside. Jim touched the middle of the controller. The portal opened into a huge chamber.

"Just **look at** that," one of the pirates **said**.

Jim and the others stepped through the portal into a room filled with gold. Flint's ship was there, too, on top of a mountain of coins.

"So, this is the 'loot of a thousand worlds,'" Silver said as he grabbed fistfuls of coins.

"Look at this," he said.

Jim found B.E.N.'s memory unit on the ship. It was clutched in the bony hand of Captain Flint's skeleton. With his memory back in place, B.E.N. remembered that Captain Flint had booby-trapped the chamber. Everything began to shake. Jim sent B.E.N. back to help Amelia and Doppler. All around Jim, tumbling mountains of gold were carrying greedy pirates into the planet's fiery core. Jim almost fell, but Silver caught him.

Jim and Silver escaped through the portal and made **it** back to the *Legacy* where B.E.N., Captain Amelia, and Dr. Doppler waited, having escaped from their guard. Jim **knew** Treasure Planet would explode in seconds, and the *Legacy* was too close.

"If **I** had a solar surfer, I **could** take this ship right through the portal," Jim **said**.

"What do **you** want Old Silver to **do**?" **John Silver** asked.

Jim told Silver what he needed. The cook used the tools on his mechanical arm to help Jim put together a surfer. Jim rode the surfer down to the controller and changed the portal just in time. The *Legacy* sailed through to peaceful space just outside Montressor Space Port.

"I knew you could do it," John Silver said.

Before the *Legacy* docked, Jim opened the hatch so Silver **could** escape in the ship's last longboat. He did not want the old scalawag to go to prison for mutiny.

Silver had found a **way** to carry away some gold coins from Treasure Planet. Before he sailed away, Silver tossed **Jim** a few of the coins. "For your dear mother, to rebuild that inn of hers," he said.

Jim's mother was waiting at the spaceport. She and Jim used the gold to rebuild the inn.

Jim entered the Interstellar Academy. He had a bright future ahead of him. He often thought about his adventure on the *Legacy*. Jim did not bring back gold from Treasure Planet, but he did **find** a treasure there. He found the courage to chart **his own** course.

Jim could find his own way.

Say the word at the top of each box. Then fill in the missing letters.

we	can
__ e	__ an
w __	ca __

Read the words in the box. Then read the sentences. Find the word in the box that correctly completes each sentence. Write the word on the line.

He _____ do it.

find
it
We
can

We like _____.

_____ do not have it.

I could not _____ it.

Trace the name with your pencil. Then write the name on your own.

Jim

Read the words in the box. Then read the sentences. Find the word in the box that correctly completes each sentence. Write the word on the line.

He was _____ .

_____ knew the way.

It _____ not her.

| He |
| gone |
| was |

ACTIVITY 4

Say the word at the top of each box. Then fill in the missing letters.

have ___ ___ve ha___ ___	the ___ ___e th___
map ___ap m___ ___	
he h___ ___e	

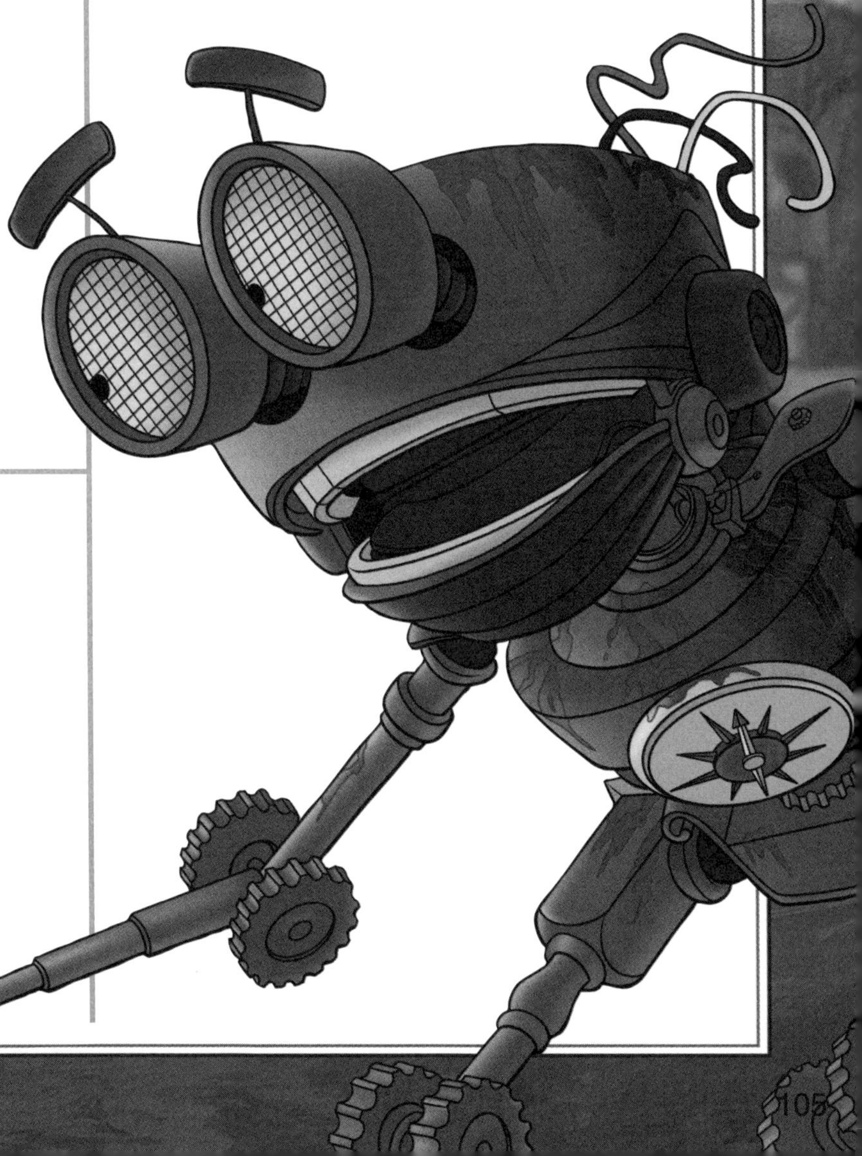

Trace each one-letter word with your pencil. Then write it on your own.

I

a

Read the words in the box. Then read the sentences. Find the word in the box that correctly completes each sentence. Write the word on the line.

_____

I have a _____ .

_____

I do not _____ the map.

_____

I can _____ this.

_____

_____ did not have it.

| do |
| have |
| place |
| He |

Say the word at the top of each box. Then fill in the missing letters.

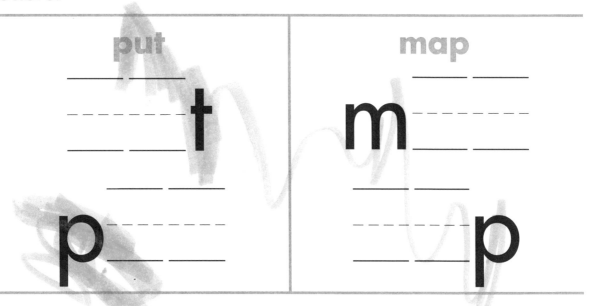

put

map

t

m

p

p

Read the words in the box. Then read the sentences. Find the word in the box that correctly completes each sentence. Write the word on the line.

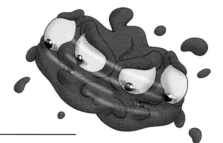

He _____ it in place.

He did not own the _____.

Jim was _____ the boat.

_____ did not look this way.

| in |
| He |
| put |
| place |

Read the words in the box. Then read the sentences. Find the word in the box that correctly completes each sentence. Write the word on the line.

_____

_____ at this.

_____

He can look _____ this map.

_____

He did not find _____ map.

this
at
Look

Trace the name with your pencil. Then write the name on your own.

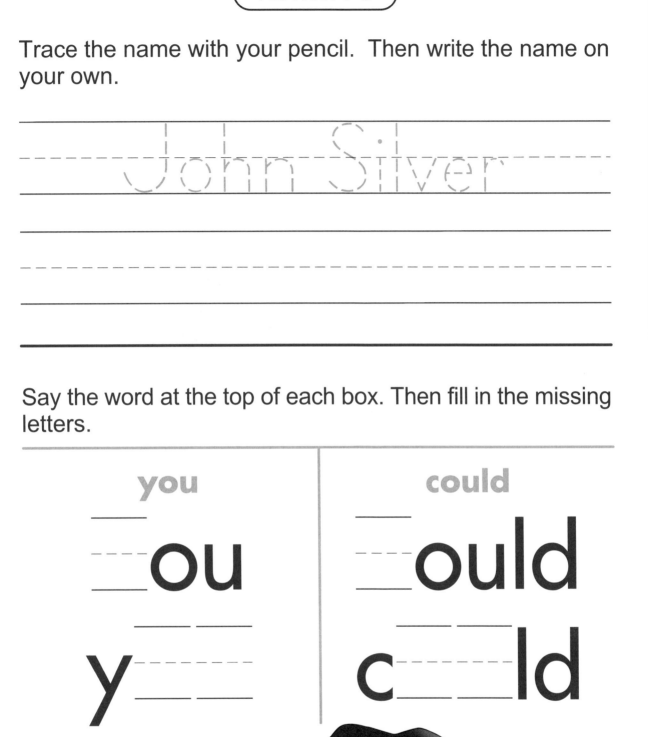

John Silver

Say the word at the top of each box. Then fill in the missing letters.

you	could
__ou	__ould
y__ __	c__ __ld

Say the word at the top of each box. Then fill in the missing letters.

own	way
___ ___ ___	___ ___ ___
___ ___ n	w ___ ___ ___
o ___ ___ ___	___ ay

Read the words in the box. Then read the sentences. Find the word in the box that correctly completes each sentence. Write the word on the line.

own

way

find

He knew the _____.

It was his _____ map.

He can _____ this.

110

a

at

can

could

did

do

find

gone

have

he

her

his

I

in

it

Jim

John Silver

knew

like

look

map

not

own

place

put

© Disney

said

© Disney

the

© Disney

this

© Disney

was

© Disney

way

© Disney

we

© Disney

you

© Disney

DISNEY'S
ATLANTIS
THE LOST EMPIRE

Adapted by Linda Armstrong

Table of Contents

Milo Thatch dreamed about finding the lost city of Atlantis. Even though others believed the city was a legend, he knew **it** was real.

Then, one day, a billionaire named Preston Whitmore sent for Milo.

"**I** have a job for you," Whitmore **said**. He handed Milo a book. "Do you know what this is?"

"It is *The Shepherd's Journal*!" Milo cried. "This is the key to finding the lost city of Atlantis. I have been looking for this book all my life."

"I am putting together a team to find Atlantis. If you decide to join the team, you **will** interpret directions and maps from this journal. What **do** you say?" Whitmore asked.

"I will do it," Milo said.

A few days later, the team was ready to go. On board their special submarine, Milo told the crew what to expect.

"First we will meet the guardian of Atlantis, a **huge** monster called the Leviathan."

At that moment the submarine crashed into something big and powerful. **It was** a giant machine.

Milo could not believe his eyes. "The Leviathan!" he cried. "How could such ancient people build a machine like this?"

"Does it matter? The thing just punched a **hole** in this submarine," Captain Rourke said.

It was a huge hole.

The team moved into smaller submarines just in time. Milo guided them through a hidden tunnel **to** an underwater air pocket. The crew set up camp. They had work to do before they could go on.

Late that night when everyone else was asleep, Milo got up. His flashlight woke up some sleeping fireflies. They fluttered down toward the camp. Everywhere they landed, a fire started. Soon, all of the tents were burning. "Fire!" shouted Milo, and everyone woke up.

"**Move** it out," ordered Rourke.

The drivers **started** their trucks.

The team started to move.

"Get these trucks over **that** bridge, on the double," Rourke shouted.

The first truck was almost across the bridge when a fuel truck blew up. One end of the bridge collapsed. All of the trucks slid down. They landed in a bed of ash in a sleeping volcano.

Milo was hurt in the fall. Strange masked figures appeared. **They** looked **at** Milo's wounds. One of the masked figures healed him with a crystal, and then they all slipped away. Milo went to **look** for them.

From the top of a ridge, Milo saw their city. "Atlantis," he **said**. "I knew it was real!"

When the rest of the team caught up with him, they were amazed.

"Look at that," they said.

The figures returned. One of them was a princess named **Kida**. She took the team into the city **where** they met her father, the king.

That night Milo showed Kida his book.

"Can you understand this?" Kida **asked**, amazed.

"Yes, of course," Milo said.

"Then you can read something else for me," she said. Kida led Milo to an underwater mural. The words and pictures on the mural told the history of Atlantis.

"The mural says that your city's power comes from a huge crystal. **It is** called the Heart of Atlantis," Milo said. "Energy from the Heart of Atlantis flows to the crystals you wear. The Heart of Atlantis keeps all of you alive."

"Where is it?" Kida asked.

"The answer was in the journal, but that page is missing," Milo **said**.

Commander Rourke and his friends were waiting for Milo and Kida to come **out** of the water. Rourke dangled the journal's missing page in front of Milo's eyes.

"Looking for this?" the commander asked. "The Heart of Atlantis is going to make us a lot of money."

"You cannot take that Crystal. These people will die without it," Milo said.

"Watch me," Commander Rourke said. **He** signaled to his friends. They grabbed Milo, Kida, and the king. Rourke took his prisoners away to the king's secret cave.

The Heart of Atlantis shot beams of light down into the cave. One of them focused on Kida. She felt herself being pulled up into the beam, and she became part of the Crystal.

When Kida came down, the commander and his assistant were ready to **move**. They locked Kida up in a special metal pod. They loaded the pod on a truck, and Rourke climbed in.

"Move out," he said.

Most members of the team agreed that Rourke was wrong to take Kida away. "We will stay with you, Milo," they said.

The old king was dying. The team's doctor **went** to **him**, but it was too late. The king gave **Milo** his crystal.

"You must bring Kida back. If she remains joined with the Heart of Atlantis, she will never break free. Her fate and the fate of Atlantis lie in your hands," the king said.

Milo showed his friends how to work the fishlike Atlantean vehicles. They zoomed off **after** Rourke. The commander had a hot air balloon. He tried to get away through the top of the volcano, but his balloon caught fire.

Milo went after him.

Rourke swung an ax at Milo, but he missed and hit Kida's pod instead. A glowing piece of crystal broke off the pod. Milo picked **it** up and cut Rourke with it. Milo **was** astonished when the commander turned to crystal, then crumbled into ash.

Rourke was gone, but Milo and his friends were not **safe**. The sleeping volcano had rumbled back to life. Milo and his friends raced back to the city just ahead of a raging river of red-hot lava. Milo opened Kida's pod. Kida drifted up to a spot high above Atlantis. Stone giants rose up out of the water. They formed a barrier that kept the hot lava out of the city.

It was safe.

The Heart of Atlantis stayed up in the sky, but the human form of Kida drifted down into Milo's arms.

It was time for the team to **leave**. The surviving team members went back to Mr. Whitmore's mansion.

"Did you find Atlantis?" **he** asked.

"The submarine sank," they said. "Milo and the others were killed. We were lucky to escape. We **did not** find Atlantis."

They handed Mr. Whitmore a small package from Milo. It was a note written on a picture. There was a crystal, too.

Mr. Whitmore understood. "At least Milo is in a better place," he said.

It was true. With Kida at his side, Milo was happy in Atlantis.

He did not leave.

Trace the name with your pencil. Then write the name on your own.

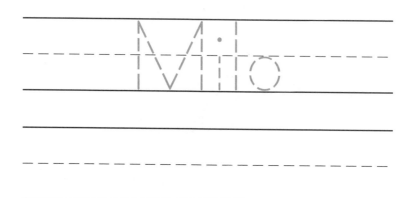

Read the words in the box. Then read the sentences. Find the word in the box that correctly completes each sentence. Write the word on the line.

He _____ do it.

He _____ he did it.

Milo will move _____.

I will _____ it.

said

do

will

it

Say the word at the top of each box. Then fill in the missing letters.

it

_ t

i _

was

_ as

w _

huge

_ uge

h _ g

hole

_ ole

h _ l

Read the words in the box. Then read the sentences. Find the word in the box that correctly completes each sentence. Write the word on the line.

They started to _____.

The _____ was not safe.

He went after _____ team.

The team _____ to leave.

He said _____ move.

team
move
to
started
the

Say the word at the top of each box. Then fill in the missing letters.

that	they
_____ _____at	_____ _____ th_____
th_____	_____ _____ey

Read the words in the box. Then read the sentences. Find the word in the box that correctly completes each sentence. Write the word on the line.

Look at _____.

I did not _____.

Look _____ that hole.

They _____ to look at it.

look
at
said
that

143

Trace the name with your pencil. Then write the name on your own.

Say the word at the top of each box. Then fill in the missing letters.

where	is
_ _ _	_
_ _ _ ere	_ s
wh_r_	i_

it	
_ t	
i_	

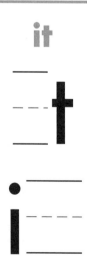

144

Read the words in the box. Then read the sentences. Find the word in the box that correctly completes each sentence. Write the word on the line.

_____

He will move _____.

_____

He _____ to move.

_____

_____ will not move.

_____

Milo will not _____ it.

move
out
He
said

Say the word at the top of each box. Then fill in the missing letters.

after	him
aft _ _ _	h _ _
a _ _ er	_ _ m

Read the words in the box. Then read the sentences. Find the word in the box that correctly completes each sentence. Write the word on the line.

_____

Milo went _____ him.

_____

He _____ to the hole.

_____

I did not leave _____ .

went

after

him

Say the word at the top of each box. Then fill in the missing letters.

it

i ____
____ t

was

____ as
w ____

safe

____ afe
s ____ f ____

147

Say the word at the top of each box. Then fill in the missing letters.

did	not
__ __id __ __ d__ __	__ __n__ __ __ __t

Read the words in the box. Then read the sentences. Find the word in the box that correctly completes each sentence. Write the word on the line.

Milo will _____ .

He _____ not do that.

Milo will _____ move out.

_____ said they went out.

He
not
did
leave

148

∧
a

∧
after

∧
asked

∧
at

∧
did

∧
do

∧
he

∧
him

Λ

Λ

Λ

Λ

Λ

Λ

Λ

Λ

∧ hole

∧ huge

© Disney

© Disney

∧ I

∧ is

© Disney

© Disney

∧ it

∧ Kida

© Disney

© Disney

∧ leave

∧ look

© Disney

© Disney

Λ

_____

- - - - - - - - - - - - - -

_____

Λ

_____

- - - - - - - - - - - - - -

_____

Λ

_____

- - - - - - - - - - - - - -

_____

Λ

_____

- - - - - - - - - - - - - -

_____

Λ

_____

- - - - - - - - - - - - - -

_____

Λ

_____

- - - - - - - - - - - - - -

_____

Λ

_____

- - - - - - - - - - - - - -

_____

Λ

_____

- - - - - - - - - - - - - -

_____

Milo

© Disney

move

© Disney

not

© Disney

out

© Disney

safe

© Disney

said

© Disney

started

© Disney

team

© Disney

Λ

Λ

Λ

Λ

Λ

Λ

Λ

Λ

^ **that**

^ **the**

^ **they**

^ **to**

^ **was**

^ **went**

^ **where**

^ **will**

A

A

A

A

A

A

A

A

Disney's Aladdin

Adapted by Linda Armstrong

Table of Contents

"Get him, Rajah!" Princess Jasmine shouted. "I want to see him **run**."

The surprised prince raced away from her pet tiger, but he was not fast enough. When Rajah took a big bite out of his pants, Princess Jasmine laughed.

"It is not funny," said Jasmine's father, the Sultan. "You must marry a prince before your next birthday. It is the law."

"That law is not fair," Jasmine said. **She wanted to** marry for love.

The next day, Princess Jasmine put her fine clothes **away**. In disguise, she climbed over the palace wall.

She wanted to run away.

Princess Jasmine visited the marketplace. She chose a fine apple from one of the stands. **She** handed it to a hungry child.

"Where is my money?" the apple seller demanded.

Jasmine **could not** pay him.

When she started to leave, he put out his hand to **stop** her. "If you take my apples, you must pay for **them**," he said. "If you cannot pay, you are a thief."

Jasmine was terrified. She did not know what to do. Then a handsome young man appeared. He helped her get away. He led her through narrow streets to safety. The two of them laughed and talked at his rooftop home. Suddenly palace guards broke in. They grabbed him.

"Let him go," Jasmine ordered. "I am the princess."

"I am sorry. These orders come from Jafar," the guard said. Jasmine knew that the Sultan's advisor was very powerful. The guards arrested her new friend.

She could not stop them.

Jasmine's new friend, Aladdin, and his pet monkey, Abu, sat in the palace dungeon. Another prisoner said he needed Aladdin's help to get a great treasure. When Aladdin agreed to help, the old man pushed on a stone, and a door opened up. The old man led Aladdin to a cave in the desert.

"Who disturbs my slumber?" the cave asked.

"It is I, Aladdin," Aladdin said.

"Proceed. Touch nothing but the lamp," said the cave.

"Fetch me the lamp," said the old man. "Then you shall have your reward."

In the cave, Aladdin and Abu met a Magic Carpet. It followed them through rooms filled with treasure. At last Aladdin found the lamp. Unfortunately, Abu **could not** resist a huge ruby. When he touched it, the whole cave started to shake. **They** rode the Magic Carpet to the cave entrance, which was starting to close. Aladdin climbed up and handed the old man the lamp. Instead of rewarding Aladdin, the old man tried to stab him. When Abu bit the attacker's wrist, the old man dropped Aladdin and Abu back into the cave, but not before Abu grabbed the lamp. The entrance closed over them. They tried to get out.

They could not.

Aladdin sat on the cave floor staring at the battered, old lamp. He wondered why the old man wanted **it**. The cave had so many real treasures. Aladdin rubbed the dusty lamp.

Poof! A big, blue Genie came out of the lamp.

"What is your first wish, Master?" the Genie asked.

"What do you mean?" Aladdin asked.

"I am the Genie of the lamp. You are my master. I will grant you three wishes. Just say what you want," the Genie said.

Aladdin did not believe him. "Some Genie. He cannot even get us out of here," he said.

"Excuse me?" said the Genie. He called the Magic Carpet, and they all climbed on. The Genie opened up a crack in the cave. Then they sailed out into the open air.

Aladdin thought about what to wish for next. There was only one thing he really wanted.

"I want to be a prince so I can marry Jasmine," he **said**.

"**Is** that your wish?" the Genie asked.

"It is," Aladdin said.

As soon as he made the wish, Aladdin became Prince Ali. The Genie wanted to **show** everyone how important Aladdin was, so he created a huge parade. Aladdin rode on the back of an elephant and tossed gold coins to the crowd.

After the parade, Aladdin went to see Princess Jasmine, but she thought he was just another spoiled prince. She would not **let** him stay.

Later that night, he rode up to her balcony on the Magic Carpet. "Princess Jasmine?" **he** called.

"Who is there?" she asked.

"Prince Ali," he said. She came closer and looked deep into his eyes.

"**You** remind **me** of someone," she **said**.

"Would you like to ride on the Magic Carpet?" he asked.

"How does it work?" she asked.

"Let me show you," he said.

Aladdin and Jasmine soared out over the city. When they returned, Jasmine was in love.

Jafar saw **it** all. **He** called the palace guards. "Get rid of that prince," he ordered.

The guards **took** Aladdin and threw him over a cliff into the ocean.

At that very moment Jasmine went **to** see her father. "I want to marry Prince Ali," she said.

"What excellent news," her father said.

"That is impossible. Prince Ali is gone," said Jafar.

"No, I am not gone. I am here," Aladdin said. The Genie had saved him.

Jafar swept out of the room, but not before he spotted the lamp hidden in Aladdin's robe.

Later that night, **Jafar** tricked Aladdin into leaving his room. Jafar's parrot flew into the room and found the lamp.

He took it to Jafar.

When Jafar rubbed the lamp, he became the master. Now, the Genie had to **work** for him.

"Make me into the Sultan," he ordered. Then he became the Sultan, but it was not enough.

"Make me into the most powerful sorcerer in the world," Jafar ordered, and he was. He used his new magical powers to send Aladdin off to a land of snow and ice.

But it was still not enough for Jafar.

"Make Jasmine fall in love with me," he ordered.

"Uh, boss, I cannot do that," said the Genie, but Jafar **did not** listen.

Meanwhile, the Magic Carpet carried Aladdin back to the palace. Jasmine saw him hiding behind a column. He was waiting for the right time to come out. The Genie could not make anyone fall in love, but Jasmine had a **plan**. She pretended **that** she was in love with Jafar.

That plan did not work.

Jasmine pulled Jafar in to kiss him. Then he saw Aladdin's reflection in her shiny crown.

"I **think** you have betrayed me," Jafar said. "And now you will pay."

He cast a spell that trapped Jasmine inside a huge hourglass. Sand poured down all around her. **Aladdin had to** do something **fast**, or Jasmine would be buried alive.

When Aladdin tried to stab Jafar, the sorcerer changed himself into a huge snake. The snake knocked the sword out of Aladdin's hands. Its coils tightened around him.

Aladdin had to think fast.

"You are powerful, but not as powerful as the Genie," he said.

Jafar, the snake, loosened his coils. "You are right," he said. "Genie, **I** am ready to make my third wish. I wish to be an all-powerful Genie."

The Genie raised his arms.

The snake began to change. Jafar the Genie grew and grew until he filled the room. "Oh, what amazing power," he said. **Then** he screamed. The lamp sucked him down inside.

"Great big powers, itty bitty living space," Aladdin said.

When Jafar was gone, **Aladdin** smashed the hourglass and saved **Jasmine**.

Finally, Aladdin faced Jasmine and her father. "I have something to tell you," he **said**. "I am not really Prince Ali. I am just Aladdin. I cannot marry the princess."

"I think my daughter was right about that law," the Sultan said. "It was not fair. Jasmine may **pick** anyone she wants to be her husband."

"Then I pick Aladdin," Jasmine said.

Say the word at the top of each box. Then fill in the missing letters.

run	away
r __ n	__ way
__ u __	aw __ __

Read the words in the box. Then read the sentences. Find the word in the box that correctly completes each sentence. Write the word on the line.

_____

She could _____ fast.

_____

_____ wanted to run.

She did not run _____.

She _____ to run.

wanted
She
away
run

178

Say the word at the top of each box. Then fill in the missing letters.

could

cou___ ___ ___

c___ ___ld

not

n___t

___o___

stop

___ ___ ___op

st___ ___ ___

them

___ ___ ___em

th___ ___ ___

Say the word at the top of each box. Then fill in the missing letters.

they	could
th___ ___ey	c___ld cou___

Read the words in the box. Then read the sentences. Find the word in the box that correctly completes each sentence. Write the word on the line.

They
not
could

_____ did not run.

They did _____ show it to him.

They _____ not work.

Trace the name with your pencil. Then write the name on your own.

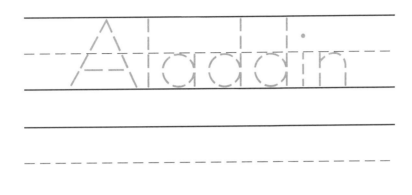

Read the words in the box. Then read the sentences. Find the word in the box that correctly completes each sentence. Write the word on the line.

_____

Aladdin _____ to run.

| is |
| it |
| said |

It ____ Aladdin.

Aladdin said to stop ____.

Read the words in the box. Then read the sentences. Find the word in the box that correctly completes each sentence. Write the word on the line.

He could not stop _____ .

_____ let me run away.

He did not _____ me stop.

He wanted to _____ me.

show
He
me
let

Trace the name with your pencil. Then write the name on your own.

Say the word at the top of each box. Then fill in the missing letters.

he	took
h____	____oo____
____e	t____k

it	
____t	
i____	

Read the words in the box. Then read the sentences. Find the word in the box that correctly completes each sentence. Write the word on the line.

_____ did not work.

Jafar's plan did not _____.

That is _____ work.

He _____ not run.

work
did
That
not

Say the word at the top of each box. Then fill in the missing letters.

think	fast
th_nk	f__st
thi___	fa___

Read the words in the box. Then read the sentences. Find the word in the box that correctly completes each sentence. Write the word on the line.

Aladdin had to _____.

He wanted to run _____.

He had _____ show them.

Aladdin _____ to stop.

had
think
fast
to

Trace the name with your pencil. Then write the name on your own.

Jasmine _____

Say the word at the top of each box. Then fill in the missing letters.

then	
___ ___ ___ ___ ___ en th ___ ___	
pick	**I**
p ___ ck pi ___ ___	

Aladdin

away

could

did

fast

had

he

I

is

it

Jafar

Jasmine

let

me

not

pick

plan

run

said

she

show

stop

that

them

then

© Disney

they

© Disney

think

© Disney

to

© Disney

took

© Disney

wanted

© Disney

work

© Disney

you

© Disney

Adapted by Linda Armstrong

Table of Contents

The great day had finally arrived! Jasmine and Aladdin were to be married.

Aladdin was filled with joy, but he was also sad. He **missed** having **his father** with him.

"I will take the dagger my father left me when he died," he said to the Genie. Carefully, he lifted it from its box and held it up.

"Father, I wish you could see me now," he said.

Aladdin missed his father.

The wedding had just started when something terrible happened. Forty thieves snuck into the room. Their leader ran to a table where the wedding gifts were displayed. He grabbed one of the gifts, a staff containing a spirit called the Oracle. The Oracle knew all things and could answer one question for each person.

Aladdin yelled, "Stop, thief!" The Oracle fell from their hands, and the thieves **ran off**.

Aladdin spoke to the Oracle, "Tell me about my past."

"Your father knows about your past," the Oracle said in an echoing voice. "The trail of the Forty Thieves will lead you **to him**."

"Hurry, Aladdin! Follow them. You must **find** your father," Princess Jasmine said.

Aladdin ran off to find him.

Aladdin **flew** after **the thieves** on the Magic Carpet. Galloping toward the sea, the thieves were already far ahead, but he caught up with them just before they reached the shore. **He** thought they were trapped. Just then, the leader raised his arm high into the air, and the sea split in two. Aladdin gasped. He had never seen anything like it. A giant rock **in** the water cracked open, and the thieves rode in one **after** another.

He flew in after the thieves.

The opening in the rock closed behind him. Aladdin was trapped inside the den of the Forty Thieves. **He** was shocked to discover that the thieves were not holding his father captive. Aladdin's **father** was the infamous King of Thieves himself!

When the King of Thieves saw Aladdin's dagger, he knew Aladdin was his son. The thieves **wanted to** kill Aladdin because he knew about their hiding place. "He must die!" they chanted. Sa'Luk, the fiercest of all the thieves, challenged Aladdin. After a fierce battle, Sa'Luk tumbled off a cliff. Although Sa'Luk escaped, everyone believed Aladdin had killed him.

One thief held out his hand to Aladdin and said, "You fought well. Welcome to the Forty Thieves."

"No, I must return home. Jasmine is waiting," Aladdin **said**. Turning to **his** father, Aladdin asked, "Will you come back with me? I want you with me when I marry Jasmine."

His father said he wanted to.

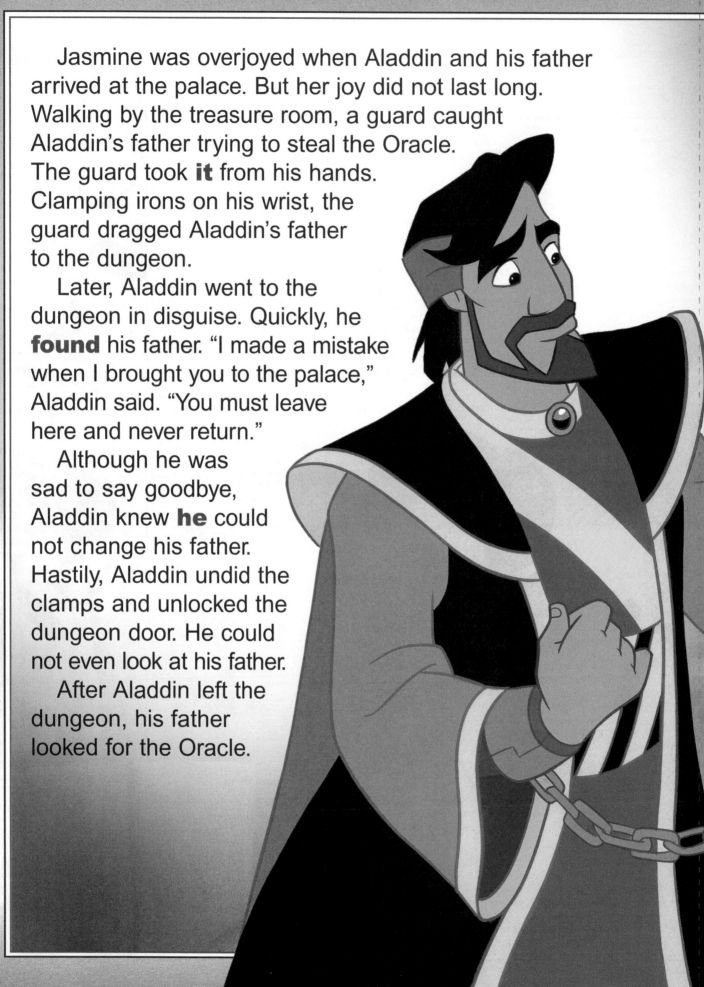

Jasmine was overjoyed when Aladdin and his father arrived at the palace. But her joy did not last long. Walking by the treasure room, a guard caught Aladdin's father trying to steal the Oracle. The guard took **it** from his hands. Clamping irons on his wrist, the guard dragged Aladdin's father to the dungeon.

Later, Aladdin went to the dungeon in disguise. Quickly, he **found** his father. "I made a mistake when I brought you to the palace," Aladdin said. "You must leave here and never return."

Although he was sad to say goodbye, Aladdin knew **he** could not change his father. Hastily, Aladdin undid the clamps and unlocked the dungeon door. He could not even look at his father.

After Aladdin left the dungeon, his father looked for the Oracle.

He found it.

Just as everyone was saying the King of Thieves was gone forever, his parrot arrived at the palace. "Your father sent me, Aladdin. He needs your help," the bedraggled bird squawked.

"We have to help him," Aladdin said. Aladdin and his friends climbed onto the Magic Carpet, and **they** flew **away** to save the King of Thieves.

The Magic Carpet carried Aladdin and his friends to the Vanishing Isle, a mysterious island where the golden Hand of King Midas was kept. When they reached the Vanishing Isle, Aladdin **ran** up some stairs and found Sa'Luk tying up his father. Aladdin jumped down from a roof, knocking his father's enemy to the ground. Then Aladdin loosened the ropes that bound his father.

"Come with me, Aladdin," his father said.

They ran away.

209

"Where are we?" **Aladdin asked** his father.

"This is a place I have been searching for my whole life," his father answered. Then he pointed to a statue with a golden hand. "That **is** the Hand of Midas. Whatever it touches will turn to gold."

Suddenly, Aladdin understood **that** the Hand of Midas was the reason his father wanted the Oracle. The Oracle showed the thieves where the golden Hand of King Midas was kept. Aladdin threw the hand to his father, **who** was careful to catch it in his robe.

"Give me that golden hand," a voice echoed. "Or I will kill your son."

"Who is that?" Aladdin asked.

It was Sa'Luk. Aladdin's father tossed the hand to him. **They** watched as it **flew** through the air. When Sa'Luk caught it, he turned into a golden statue.

Aladdin asked his father to come **home** with him. "I will not get married without you," he said. Carefully, he removed the Hand of Midas from Sa'Luk's golden fingers. He put a cloth on it and handed it to his father.

Aladdin's father threw the hand into the ocean. "This thing almost cost me my one true treasure," he said.

Then, Aladdin and his father climbed **on the** Magic **Carpet**.

They flew home on the Carpet.

213

Aladdin's father came to the wedding, but he **was** still a wanted man, so he had to watch from behind a column. *I know my son will not make as many mistakes as I did*, he thought. *I left my family to find gold, but **Aladdin** has already found his treasure.*

Just knowing his father was there made Aladdin very **happy**. As he left the wedding **with Jasmine**, Aladdin saw his father slip away.

214

Aladdin was happy with Jasmine.

215

Trace the name with your pencil. Then write the name on your own.

Aladdin

Read the words in the box. Then read the sentences. Find the word in the box that correctly completes each sentence. Write the word on the line.

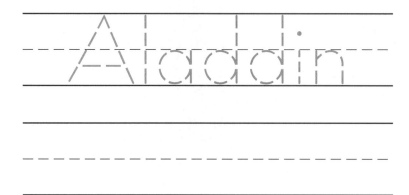

His father_____ Aladdin.

He missed his_____.

_____ missed him.

That was___ father.

| Aladdin |
| his |
| missed |
| father |

Say the word at the top of each box. Then fill in the missing letters.

him

_im

hi_

off

_ff

o__

find

fi__

__nd

to

__o

t__

Say the word at the top of each box. Then fill in the missing letters.

flew

___ ___ ___
___ ___ ___ ew
fl___ ___ ___

in

___ ___
___ ___ n
i___

after

___ ___ ___ ___ ___
a___ ___ ___ er
___ ___ ___
ft ___ ___ ___

the

___ ___ ___
___ ___ ___ e
th___ ___

thieves

___ ___ ___ ___ ___
th___ ___ ve___
___ ___ ___ ___ ___
___ ___ iev ___ s

Read the words in the box. Then read the sentences. Find the word in the box that correctly completes each sentence. Write the word on the line.

_____
_____ wanted his father.

He _____ the Carpet.

_____ father wanted to find him.

"Find the thieves," he _____ .

He wanted _____ find Aladdin.

His _____ wanted him.

wanted
father
His
said
He
to

Say the word at the top of each box. Then fill in the missing letters.

he	found
__ __	__ __ __
__e	fou__ __
h__ __	f__ __nd

Read the words in the box. Then read the sentences. Find the word in the box that correctly completes each sentence. Write the word on the line.

it
He
found

_____

_____ flew after the thieves.

The thieves _____ it.

His father wanted _____.

Say the word at the top of each box. Then fill in the missing letters.

away

aw_____

_____ay

ran

r__n

__a__

they

th____

____ey

Say the word at the top of each box. Then fill in the missing letters.

that

th___ ___

___ ___ ___

___ ___ at

who

___ ___ ___

___ ___ o

wh___ ___

is

___ ___

___ s

i___ ___

asked

___ ___ ___

a___ ___ ed

ask___ ___

222

ACTIVITY 8

Read the words in the box. Then read the sentences. Find the word in the box that correctly completes each sentence. Write the word on the line.

_____

They _____ on the Carpet.

Aladdin flew on a _____.

Aladdin flew _____.

Aladdin flew _____ the Carpet.

| flew |
| carpet |
| home |
| on |

Trace the name with your pencil. Then write the name on your own.

Jasmine

Read the words in the box. Then read the sentences. Find the word in the box that correctly completes each sentence. Write the word on the line.

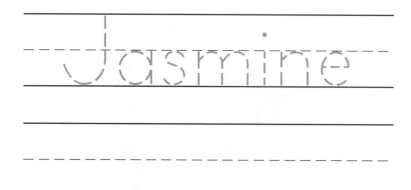

_____ was happy.

Jasmine flew off _____ him.

Aladdin was _____ .

His father _____ with him.

Jasmine
with
happy
was

after

Aladdin

asked

away

carpet

father

find

flew

found

© Disney

happy

© Disney

he

© Disney

him

© Disney

his

© Disney

home

© Disney

in

© Disney

is

© Disney

it

© Disney

Jasmine

© Disney

missed

© Disney

off

© Disney

on

© Disney

ran

© Disney

said

© Disney

that

© Disney

the

they

thieves

to

wanted

was

who

with

ANSWER KEY

ACTIVITY 1
Read the words in the box. Then read the sentences. Find the word in the box that correctly completes each sentence. Write the word on the line.

He **came** right over.

He was **right**.

He fell **down**.

Then he came down.

| right |
| came |
| Then |
| down |

Page 26

ACTIVITY 2
Say the word at the top of each box. Then fill in the missing letters.

fell	all
fe**ll**	a**ll**
f**e**ll	a**ll**

over
o**v**er
o**v**er

them
them
them

Page 27

ACTIVITY 3
Trace the name with your pencil. Then write the name on your own.

Peter Pan

Peter Pan

Say the word at the top of each box. Then fill in the missing letters.

will	get
wi**ll**	g**e**t
wi**ll**	g**e**t

Page 28

ACTIVITY 4
Trace the name with your pencil. Then write the name on your own.

Tiger Lily

Tiger Lily

Read the words in the box. Then read the sentences. Find the word in the box that correctly completes each sentence. Write the word on the line.

He **said** I could get it.

I came right over.

I will **not** get it.

He **will** get them.

| not |
| said |
| will |
| I |

Page 29

ACTIVITY 5
Say the word at the top of each box. Then fill in the missing letters.

he	saved
h**e**	s**a**ved
h**e**	s**a**ved

Read the words in the box. Then read the sentences. Find the word in the box that correctly completes each sentence. Write the word on the line.

He saved them.

He **saved** Tiger Lily.

| saved |
| He |

Page 30

ACTIVITY 6
Say the word at the top of each box. Then fill in the missing letters.

they	could
th**e**y	cou**l**d
th**e**y	cou**l**d

not
n**o**t
n**o**t

away
a**w**ay
a**w**ay

Page 31

ACTIVITY 7
Say the word at the top of each box. Then fill in the missing letters.

got	out
g**o**t	o**u**t
g**o**t	ou**t**

Read the words in the box. Then read the sentences. Find the word in the box that correctly completes each sentence. Write the word on the line.

Peter Pan **got** them out.

He came right **out**.

It was the right **way**.

He saw **the** way out.

| the |
| got |
| way |
| out |

Page 32

ACTIVITY 8
Trace the word with your pencil. Then write the word on your own.

crocodile

crocodile

Read the words in the box. Then read the sentences. Find the word in the box that correctly completes each sentence. Write the word on the line.

Peter Pan was **behind** him.

He was **right** behind Peter Pan.

It **was** not right.

They saved **him**.

| behind |
| was |
| him |
| right |

Page 33

ACTIVITY 9
Say the word at the top of each box. Then fill in the missing letters.

saw	it
s**a**w	i**t**
s**a**w	i**t**

Read the words in the box. Then read the sentences. Find the word in the box that correctly completes each sentence. Write the word on the line.

He **saw** all of them.

They saw it.

It was not Tiger Lily.

They **all** got out.

| all |
| They |
| It |
| saw |

Page 34

ANSWER KEY

ACTIVITY 1
Trace the name with your pencil. Then write the name on your own.

Jane   Jane

Page 64

ACTIVITY 2
Say the word at the top of each box. Then fill in the missing letters.

her	away
her	away
her	away

Read the words in the box. Then read the sentences. Find the word in the box that correctly completes each sentence. Write the word on the line.

He _took_ it.

She took it _away_.

_He_ flew away.

He took _her_ away.

He away took her

Page 65

ACTIVITY 3
Trace the name with your pencil. Then write the name on your own.

Peter Pan
Peter Pan

Read the words in the box. Then read the sentences. Find the word in the box that correctly completes each sentence. Write the word on the line.

I did not _believe_ it.

Jane _cannot_ believe it.

Jane _said_ she did not believe it.

I said I did not like _it_.

cannot believe it said

Page 66

ACTIVITY 4
Say the word at the top of each box. Then fill in the missing letters.

because

because
because

cannot

cannot
cannot

fly	said
fly	said
fly	said

Page 67

ACTIVITY 5
Read the words in the box. Then read the sentences. Find the word in the box that correctly completes each sentence. Write the word on the line.

Jane _did_ not like Peter Pan.

She cannot fly.

It will _not_ fly away.

She did not _like_ him.

like not She did

Page 68

ACTIVITY 6
Trace the name with your pencil. Then write the name on your own.

Captain Hook
Captain Hook

Say the word at the top of each box. Then fill in the missing letters.

then	came
then	came
then	came

Page 69

ACTIVITY 7
Read the words in the box. Then read the sentences. Find the word in the box that correctly completes each sentence. Write the word on the line.

Jane _set_ them free.

She cannot set it _free_.

She took _them_.

Then _she_ set it free.

free them she set

Page 70

ACTIVITY 8
Say the word at the top of each box. Then fill in the missing letters.

with	flew
with	flew

Read the words in the box. Then read the sentences. Find the word in the box that correctly completes each sentence. Write the word on the line.

He _flew_ away.

Peter Pan flew _away_.

Jane took it _with_ her.

away flew with

Page 71

ACTIVITY 9
Read the words in the box. Then read the sentences. Find the word in the box that correctly completes each sentence. Write the word on the line.

They _both_ flew away.

They like to fly.

He _flew_ away.

She did not like _to_ fly.

both flew They to

Page 72

ANSWER KEY

ACTIVITY 1

Say the word at the top of each box. Then fill in the missing letters.

we	can
we	can
we	can

Read the words in the box. Then read the sentences. Find the word in the box that correctly completes each sentence. Write the word on the line.

He **can** do it.

We like **it**.

We do not have it.

I could not **find** it.

> find
> it
> we
> can

Page 102

ACTIVITY 2

Trace the name with your pencil. Then write the name on your own.

Jim   Jim

Page 103

ACTIVITY 3

Read the words in the box. Then read the sentences. Find the word in the box that correctly completes each sentence. Write the word on the line.

He was **gone**.

He knew the way.

It **was** not her.

> He
> gone
> was

Page 104

ACTIVITY 4

Say the word at the top of each box. Then fill in the missing letters.

have	the
have	the

map	
map	

he	
he	

Page 105

ACTIVITY 5

Trace each one-letter word with your pencil. Then write it on your own.

I	a
I	a

Read the words in the box. Then read the sentences. Find the word in the box that correctly completes each sentence. Write the word on the line.

I have a **place**.

I do not **have** the map.

I can **do** this.

He did not have it.

> do
> have
> place
> He

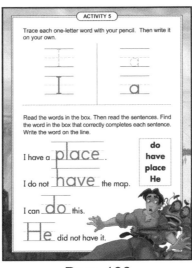

Page 106

ACTIVITY 6

Say the word at the top of each box. Then fill in the missing letters.

put	map
put	map

Read the words in the box. Then read the sentences. Find the word in the box that correctly completes each sentence. Write the word on the line.

He **put** it in place.

He did not own the **place**.

Jim was **in** the boat.

He did not look this way.

> in
> He
> put
> place

Page 107

ACTIVITY 7

Read the words in the box. Then read the sentences. Find the word in the box that correctly completes each sentence. Write the word on the line.

Look at this.

He can look **at** this map.

He did not find **this** map.

> this
> at
> Look

Page 108

ACTIVITY 8

Trace the name with your pencil. Then write the name on your own.

John Silver

John Silver

Say the word at the top of each box. Then fill in the missing letters.

you	could
you	could

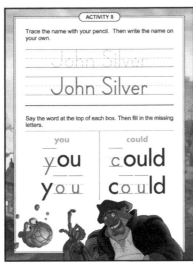

Page 109

ACTIVITY 9

Say the word at the top of each box. Then fill in the missing letters.

own	way
own	way

Read the words in the box. Then read the sentences. Find the word in the box that correctly completes each sentence. Write the word on the line.

He knew the **way**.

It was his **own** map.

He can **find** this.

> own
> way
> find

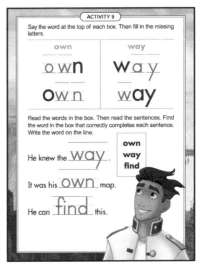

Page 110

ANSWER KEY

ACTIVITY 1

Trace the name with your pencil. Then write the name on your own.

Milo

Milo

Read the words in the box. Then read the sentences. Find the word in the box that correctly completes each sentence. Write the word on the line.

He __will__ do it.

He __said__ he did it.

Milo will move __it__.

I will __do__ it.

said
do
will
it

Page 140

ACTIVITY 2

Say the word at the top of each box. Then fill in the missing letters.

it
__it__
__it__

was
__was__
__was__

huge
__huge__
__huge__

hole
__hole__
__hole__

Page 141

ACTIVITY 3

Read the words in the box. Then read the sentences. Find the word in the box that correctly completes each sentence. Write the word on the line.

They started to __move__.

The __team__ was not safe.

He went after __the__ team.

The team __started__ to leave.

He said __to__ move.

team
move
to
started
the

Page 142

ACTIVITY 4

Say the word at the top of each box. Then fill in the missing letters.

that
__that__
__that__

they
__they__
__they__

Read the words in the box. Then read the sentences. Find the word in the box that correctly completes each sentence. Write the word on the line.

Look at __that__.

I did not __look__.

Look __at__ that hole.

They __said__ to look at it.

look
at
said
that

Page 143

ACTIVITY 5

Trace the name with your pencil. Then write the name on your own.

Kida   Kida

Say the word at the top of each box. Then fill in the missing letters.

where
__where__
__where__

is
__is__
__is__

it
__it__
__it__

Page 144

ACTIVITY 6

Read the words in the box. Then read the sentences. Find the word in the box that correctly completes each sentence. Write the word on the line.

He will move __out__.

He __said__ to move.

__He__ will not move.

Milo will not __move__ it.

move
out
He
said

Page 145

ACTIVITY 7

Say the word at the top of each box. Then fill in the missing letters.

after
__after__

him
__him__

Read the words in the box. Then read the sentences. Find the word in the box that correctly completes each sentence. Write the word on the line.

Milo went __after__ him.

He __went__ to the hole.

I did not leave __him__.

went
after
him

Page 146

ACTIVITY 8

Say the word at the top of each box. Then fill in the missing letters.

it
__it__
__it__

was
__was__
__was__

safe
__safe__
__safe__

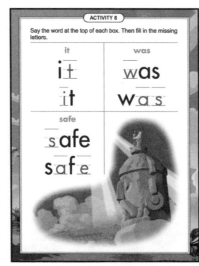

Page 147

ACTIVITY 9

Say the word at the top of each box. Then fill in the missing letters.

did
__did__
__did__

not
__not__
__not__

Read the words in the box. Then read the sentences. Find the word in the box that correctly completes each sentence. Write the word on the line.

Milo will __leave__.

He __did__ not do that.

Milo will __not__ move out.

__He__ said they went out.

He
not
did
leave

Page 148

236

ANSWER KEY

ACTIVITY 1

Say the word at the top of each box. Then fill in the missing letters.

run	away
run	away
run	away

Read the words in the box. Then read the sentences. Find the word in the box that correctly completes each sentence. Write the word on the line.

She could **run** fast.

She wanted to run.

She did not run **away**.

She **wanted** to run.

> wanted
> She
> away
> run

Page 178

ACTIVITY 2

Say the word at the top of each box. Then fill in the missing letters.

could	not
could	not
could	not
stop	them
stop	them
stop	them

Page 179

ACTIVITY 3

Say the word at the top of each box. Then fill in the missing letters.

they	could
they	could
they	could

Read the words in the box. Then read the sentences. Find the word in the box that correctly completes each sentence. Write the word on the line.

They did not run.

They did not **not** show it to him.

They **could** not work.

> They
> not
> could

Page 180

ACTIVITY 4

Trace the name with your pencil. Then write the name on your own.

Aladdin

Aladdin

Read the words in the box. Then read the sentences. Find the word in the box that correctly completes each sentence. Write the word on the line.

Aladdin **said** to run.

It **is** Aladdin.

Aladdin said to stop **it**.

> is
> it
> said

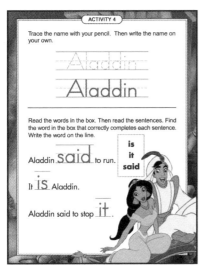

Page 181

ACTIVITY 5

Read the words in the box. Then read the sentences. Find the word in the box that correctly completes each sentence. Write the word on the line.

He could not stop **me**.

He let me run away.

He did not **let** me stop.

He wanted to **show** me.

> show
> He
> me
> let

Page 182

ACTIVITY 6

Trace the name with your pencil. Then write the name on your own.

Jafar   Jafar

Say the word at the top of each box. Then fill in the missing letters.

he	took
he	took
he	took
it	
it	
it	

Page 183

ACTIVITY 7

Read the words in the box. Then read the sentences. Find the word in the box that correctly completes each sentence. Write the word on the line.

That did not work.

Jafar's plan did not **work**.

That is **not** work.

He **did** not run.

> work
> did
> That
> not

Page 184

ACTIVITY 8

Say the word at the top of each box. Then fill in the missing letters.

think	fast
think	fast
think	fast

Read the words in the box. Then read the sentences. Find the word in the box that correctly completes each sentence. Write the word on the line.

Aladdin had to **think**.

He wanted to run **fast**.

He had **to** show them.

Aladdin **had** to stop.

> had
> think
> fast
> to

Page 185

ACTIVITY 9

Trace the name with your pencil. Then write the name on your own.

Jasmine   Jasmine

Say the word at the top of each box. Then fill in the missing letters.

then	
then	
then	
pick	I
pick	I
pick	I

Page 186

ANSWER KEY

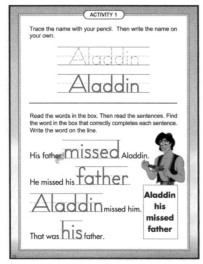

238